# Recipes

PRETTY SIMPLE BOOKS

## EMAIL US AT

prettysimplebooks@gmail.com

## TO GET FREE GOODIES!

Just title the email "Recipe Book Freebie"
And we will send some extra surprises your way!

Recipe Book

From the kitchen of:

Chelsea

# Conversion Chart

## DRY MEASURMENTS:

| | | |
|---|---|---|
| 3 tsp | 1 Tbsp | 1/16 C |
| 6 tsp | 2 Tbsp | 1/8 C |
| 12 tsp | 4 Tbsp | 1/4 C |
| 16 tsp | 5 Tbsp + 1 tsp | 1/3 C |
| 24 tsp | 8 Tbsp | 1/2 C |
| 32 tsp | 10 Tbsp + 2 tsp | 2/3 C |
| 36 tsp | 12 Tbsp | 3/4 C |
| 48 tsp | 16 Tbsp | 1 C |

## LIQUID MEASUREMENTS:

| | | |
|---|---|---|
| 1 gal | 4 qts | 3.8 liters |
| 4 cups | 1 qt | .95 liters |
| 2 cups | 1 pt | 473 ml |
| 1 C | 8 oz | 237 ml |
| 3/4 C | 6 oz | 177 ml |
| 2/3 C | 5 1/3 oz | 158 ml |
| 1/2 C | 4 oz | 118 ml |
| 1/3 C | 2 2/3 oz | 79 ml |
| 1/4 C | 2 oz | 59 ml |
| 1/8 C | 1 oz | 30 ml |
| 1/16 C | 1/2 oz | 15 ml |

## TEMP:

| °F | °C |
|---|---|
| 475 | 245 |
| 450 | 230 |
| 425 | 220 |
| 400 | 200 |
| 375 | 190 |
| 350 | 177 |
| 325 | 165 |
| 300 | 150 |
| 250 | 120 |

## WEIGHT:

| | |
|---|---|
| 1/2 oz | 14 g |
| 1 oz | 28 g |
| 2 oz | 57 g |
| 3 oz | 85 g |
| 4 oz | 113 g |
| 5 oz | 141 g |
| 6 oz | 170 g |
| 7 oz | 198 g |
| 8 oz | 227 g |
| 9 oz | 255 g |
| 10 oz | 283 g |
| 11 oz | 312 g |
| 12 oz | 340 g |
| 13 oz | 369 g |
| 14 oz | 397 g |
| 15 oz | 425 g |
| 1 lb | 454 g |

# Recipe Index

crockpot = ✱

# Recipe: CHICKEN NOODLE SOUP

## Ingredients

1 bag baby carrots
1 pack celery
10 cup chicken broth
5 cups egg noodles
3 cups Rotisserie chicken

garlic to taste
salt/pepper/
rosemary to taste

## Directions

1. Saute celery, carrots
2. add garlic to taste
3. Add chicken broth, boil
4. Cook noodles and add to broth mixture
5. Add chicken
6. season to taste

**SERVES**
2   4   6   (8)   10+

**DIFFICULTY:**
(1)   2   3   4   5

**COOK TIME:**
hours: 0   min: 30

**PREP TIME:**
hours: 0   min: 30

**NOTES:**
serve warm
for 3-4 days

can freeze for
3 mo.

# Recipe: Roasted Asparagus

## Ingredients

1 LB. asparagus, trimmed
2 tbs. balsamic vinegar
1 TBS olive Oil
1/4 tsk. pepper
1/8 tsp salt.

## Directions

1. preheat to 350°
2. line sheet with foil
3. place asparagus down, drizzle with balsamic and olive oil. Season
4. cook for 20-25 min.

**SERVES** veggies per.
2 ④ 6 8 10+

**DIFFICULTY:**
① 2 3 4 5

**COOK TIME:**
hours: ____ min: 20-25

**PREP TIME:**
hours: ____ min: 5

**NOTES:**

2

# Recipe: shrimp scampi

## Ingredients

3 tbs butter, cut into pieces
2 tsp olive oil
1 tsp onion powder
1/2 tsp salt
1/4 cup of white wine

2 tsp minced garlic
1 (12oz) pkg of shrimp (medium/peeled)
1-2 tbs cilantro, parsley, thyme or chives to garnish

SERVES
2 4 6 8 10+

DIFFICULTY:
1 2 3 4 5

COOK TIME:
hours: ___ min: 10

PREP TIME:
hours: ___ min: 10

NOTES:

## Directions

1. melt butter over medium-high heat.
2. Once butter is melted, add minced garlic if desired and olive oil, garlic powder, salt, and sauté for 2 min. Pour white wine, stir frequently. Cook for 2-3 min. reduce heat.
3. add shrimp and sauté, stirring constantly. Turn each shrimp over as soon as it's pink. shrimp will be done 1-2min. remove from heat.
4. sprinkle with fresh herbs and serve.

3

# Recipe: alfredo sauce

## Ingredients

1/2 stick butter (4 TBS)
1 pint heavy cream
1 cup parm. cheese
1/2 tsp. nutmeg
1/4 tsp. salt.

1/8 tsp pepper
1 LB. pasta

## Directions

1. In a med. saucepan, melt butter over med.-high heat.
2. Stir in heavy cream and grated cheese. Stir until cheese is melted, reduce heat to med-low.
3. Season w/ nutmeg, salt, pepper.
4. Cook for 20 min.
5. Serve with pasta

SERVES (1/4 - 1/2 cup/per)
2   4   (6 - 8)   10+

DIFFICULTY:
1   2   3   4   5

COOK TIME:
hours: ___   min: 25

PREP TIME:
hours: ___   min: 5

NOTES:

# Recipe: marinara sauce

## Ingredients

- 1 TBS Butter
- 2 tsp. olive oil
- 1 med. onion
- 2 tsp. garlic
- 1 cup cab. sauvignon
- 2 (28 oz) crushed tomatoes
- 1 (6 oz) tomato paste
- 3 tbs granulated sugar
- 1 TBS stir in basil paste
- 1 tsp italian seasoning
- 1 tsp oregano
- 1 tsp salt, 1/2 tsp pepper

SERVES (8 cups)

2   4   6   (8)   10+

DIFFICULTY:

1   2   3   4   5

COOK TIME:

hours: ___   min: 27-35

PREP TIME:

hours: ___   min: 10

NOTES:

## Directions

1. preheat a medium pot over high heat for 1 min. add butter and olive oil, heat for 1-2 min

2. add onion and garlic, sauté for 3-4 min until golden and softened.

3. stir in wine, crushed tomatoes, tomato paste, sugar & seasonings. Reduce heat to medium high. cook, stir occasionally. for 20-30 min. Serve with pasta.

⑤ can add 1/2 LB ground turkey or beef after onions are sautéed.

5

# Recipe: Tuscan White Bean Soup

## Ingredients

3 slices bacon, chopped
2 tbs. olive oil
2 small carrots, chopped
1/2 cup diced onion
1 med. potato peeled & cubed
4 cup. chicken broth

1 (15oz) can white navy beans, drain/rinse
salt + pepper
3 cup. spinach
parm cheese
to garnish

SERVES
2   4   6   8   10+

DIFFICULTY:
①   2   3   4   5

COOK TIME:
hours: _____   min: 35

PREP TIME:
hours: _____   min: 10

NOTES:

## Directions

1. In lrg pot over med-high heat cook bacon until strips are brown (4mm) flip with tongs and cook for 2min. transfer to paper towel to drain. Leave grease in pot.
2. add carrots, onion and potato to the pot and sauté over med-low heat until onions are translucent and veggies begin to soften, 15min.
3. pour chicken broth, add beans and season. chop/crumble bacon into pot. Bring to simmer over med heat for 10min. reduce heat and add spinach, 3min, until wilted
4. serve and top with parm cheese

# Recipe: _____

## ———— Ingredients ————

_____  _____
_____  _____
_____  _____
_____  _____
_____  _____
_____  _____

## Directions ————

SERVES
2   4   6   8   10+

DIFFICULTY:
1   2   3   4   5

COOK TIME:
hours: _____   min: _____

PREP TIME:
hours: _____   min: _____

NOTES:

# Recipe: _____

## Ingredients

_____  _____
_____  _____
_____  _____
_____  _____
_____  _____
_____

## Directions

_____
_____
_____
_____
_____
_____
_____
_____
_____
_____
_____
_____
_____
_____
_____
_____
_____
_____
_____
_____
_____

SERVES
2   4   6   8   10+

DIFFICULTY:
1   2   3   4   5

COOK TIME:
hours: _____   min: _____

PREP TIME:
hours: _____   min: _____

NOTES:

# Recipe: _____

## Ingredients

_____    _____
_____    _____
_____    _____
_____    _____
_____    _____

## Directions

_____
_____
_____
_____
_____
_____
_____
_____
_____
_____
_____
_____
_____
_____
_____
_____
_____
_____
_____
_____
_____
_____
_____

**SERVES**
2   4   6   8   10+

**DIFFICULTY:**
1   2   3   4   5

**COOK TIME:**
hours: _____   min: _____

**PREP TIME:**
hours: _____   min: _____

**NOTES:**

# Recipe: _____

## — Ingredients —

_____  _____
_____  _____
_____  _____
_____  _____
_____  _____

## Directions

_____
_____
_____
_____
_____
_____
_____
_____
_____
_____
_____
_____
_____
_____
_____
_____
_____
_____
_____
_____
_____
_____

SERVES
2   4   6   8   10+

DIFFICULTY:
1   2   3   4   5

COOK TIME:
hours: _____   min: _____

PREP TIME:
hours: _____   min: _____

NOTES:

# Recipe: _____

## Ingredients

_____   _____
_____   _____
_____   _____
_____   _____
_____   _____
_____   _____

## Directions

_____
_____
_____
_____
_____
_____
_____
_____
_____
_____
_____
_____
_____
_____
_____
_____
_____
_____
_____
_____
_____
_____
_____

SERVES
2   4   6   8   10+

DIFFICULTY:
1   2   3   4   5

COOK TIME:
hours: _____   min: _____

PREP TIME:
hours: _____   min: _____

NOTES:

# Recipe: _____

## Ingredients

_____  _____
_____  _____
_____  _____
_____  _____
_____

## Directions

_____
_____
_____
_____
_____
_____
_____
_____
_____
_____
_____
_____
_____
_____
_____
_____
_____
_____
_____
_____
_____
_____

**SERVES**

2   4   6   8   10+

**DIFFICULTY:**

1   2   3   4   5

**COOK TIME:**

hours: _____   min: _____

**PREP TIME:**

hours: _____   min: _____

**NOTES:**

# Recipe: _____

## Ingredients

_____    _____
_____    _____
_____    _____
_____    _____
_____    _____

## Directions

_____
_____
_____
_____
_____
_____
_____
_____
_____
_____
_____
_____
_____
_____
_____
_____
_____
_____
_____
_____
_____
_____

SERVES
2   4   6   8   10+

DIFFICULTY:
1    2    3    4    5

COOK TIME:
hours: _____   min: _____

PREP TIME:
hours: _____   min: _____

NOTES:

# Recipe: _____

## Ingredients

_____  _____
_____  _____
_____  _____
_____  _____

## Directions

_____
_____
_____
_____
_____
_____
_____
_____
_____
_____
_____
_____
_____
_____
_____
_____
_____
_____
_____
_____
_____
_____
_____
_____
_____

**SERVES**
2  4  6  8  10+

**DIFFICULTY:**
1  2  3  4  5

**COOK TIME:**
hours: _____  min: _____

**PREP TIME:**
hours: _____  min: _____

**NOTES:**

# Recipe: _____

## _____ Ingredients _____

_____    _____
_____    _____
_____    _____
_____    _____
_____    _____

## Directions

_____
_____
_____
_____
_____
_____
_____
_____
_____
_____
_____
_____
_____
_____
_____
_____
_____
_____
_____
_____
_____
_____
_____
_____

SERVES
2   4   6   8   10+

DIFFICULTY:
1   2   3   4   5

COOK TIME:
hours: _____   min: _____

PREP TIME:
hours: _____   min: _____

NOTES:

# Recipe: _____

## Ingredients

_____    _____
_____    _____
_____    _____
_____    _____

## Directions

_____
_____
_____
_____
_____
_____
_____
_____
_____
_____
_____
_____
_____
_____
_____
_____
_____
_____
_____

**SERVES**
2   4   6   8   10+

**DIFFICULTY:**
1   2   3   4   5

**COOK TIME:**
hours: _____   min: _____

**PREP TIME:**
hours: _____   min: _____

**NOTES:**

# Recipe: _____

## Ingredients

_____    _____
_____    _____
_____    _____
_____    _____
_____    _____
_____    _____

## Directions

_____
_____
_____
_____
_____
_____
_____
_____
_____
_____
_____
_____
_____
_____
_____
_____
_____
_____
_____
_____
_____
_____

SERVES
2   4   6   8   10+

DIFFICULTY:
1   2   3   4   5

COOK TIME:
hours: _____   min: _____

PREP TIME:
hours: _____   min: _____

NOTES:

# Recipe: _____

## —— Ingredients ——

_____ _____
_____ _____
_____ _____
_____ _____

## Directions ——

_____
_____
_____
_____
_____
_____
_____
_____
_____
_____
_____
_____
_____
_____
_____
_____
_____
_____
_____
_____
_____

**SERVES**

2   4   6   8   10+

**DIFFICULTY:**

1   2   3   4   5

**COOK TIME:**

hours: _____   min: _____

**PREP TIME:**

hours: _____   min: _____

**NOTES:**

# Recipe: _____

## Ingredients

_____  _____
_____  _____
_____  _____
_____  _____
_____  _____
_____  _____

## Directions

_____
_____
_____
_____
_____
_____
_____
_____
_____
_____
_____
_____
_____
_____
_____
_____
_____
_____
_____
_____
_____
_____
_____

SERVES

2  4  6  8  10+

DIFFICULTY:

1  2  3  4  5

COOK TIME:

hours: _____  min: _____

PREP TIME:

hours: _____  min: _____

NOTES:

# Recipe: _____

## — Ingredients —

_____  _____
_____  _____
_____  _____
_____  _____
_____  _____

## Directions

_____
_____
_____
_____
_____
_____
_____
_____
_____
_____
_____
_____
_____
_____
_____
_____
_____
_____
_____

**SERVES**

2   4   6   8   10+

**DIFFICULTY:**

1   2   3   4   5

**COOK TIME:**

hours: _____   min: _____

**PREP TIME:**

hours: _____   min: _____

**NOTES:**

# Recipe: _____

## Ingredients

_____    _____
_____    _____
_____    _____
_____    _____
_____    _____
_____    _____

## Directions

_____
_____
_____
_____
_____
_____
_____
_____
_____
_____
_____
_____
_____
_____
_____
_____
_____
_____
_____
_____
_____

**SERVES**
2   4   6   8   10+

**DIFFICULTY:**
1    2    3    4    5

**COOK TIME:**
hours: ____    min: ____

**PREP TIME:**
hours: ____    min: ____

**NOTES:**

# Recipe: _____

## Ingredients

_____ _____

_____ _____

_____ _____

_____ _____

_____ _____

## Directions

_____

_____

_____

_____

_____

_____

_____

_____

_____

_____

_____

_____

_____

_____

_____

_____

_____

_____

_____

_____

_____

_____

**SERVES**

2   4   6   8   10+

**DIFFICULTY:**

1   2   3   4   5

**COOK TIME:**

hours: _____   min: _____

**PREP TIME:**

hours: _____   min: _____

**NOTES:**

# Recipe: _____

## Ingredients

_____  _____
_____  _____
_____  _____
_____  _____
_____  _____
_____  _____

## Directions

_____
_____
_____
_____
_____
_____
_____
_____
_____
_____
_____
_____
_____
_____
_____
_____
_____
_____
_____
_____
_____
_____

SERVES
2   4   6   8   10+

DIFFICULTY:
1   2   3   4   5

COOK TIME:
hours: _____   min: _____

PREP TIME:
hours: _____   min: _____

NOTES:

# Recipe: _____

## Ingredients

_____ _____
_____ _____
_____ _____
_____ _____
_____ _____

## Directions

_____
_____
_____
_____
_____
_____
_____
_____
_____
_____
_____
_____
_____
_____
_____
_____
_____
_____
_____
_____
_____

SERVES

2   4   6   8   10+

DIFFICULTY:

1   2   3   4   5

COOK TIME:

hours: _____   min: _____

PREP TIME:

hours: _____   min: _____

NOTES:

# Recipe: _____

## Ingredients

_____  _____
_____  _____
_____  _____
_____  _____
_____  _____

## Directions

_____
_____
_____
_____
_____
_____
_____
_____
_____
_____
_____
_____
_____
_____
_____
_____
_____
_____
_____
_____
_____
_____
_____
_____

**SERVES**
2   4   6   8   10+

**DIFFICULTY:**
1   2   3   4   5

**COOK TIME:**
hours: ____   min: ____

**PREP TIME:**
hours: ____   min: ____

**NOTES:**

# Recipe: _____

## — Ingredients —

_____  _____
_____  _____
_____  _____
_____  _____
_____

## Directions ——

_____
_____
_____
_____
_____
_____
_____
_____
_____
_____
_____
_____
_____
_____
_____
_____
_____
_____
_____
_____
_____
_____
_____

SERVES

2   4   6   8   10+

DIFFICULTY:

1   2   3   4   5

COOK TIME:

hours: _____   min: _____

PREP TIME:

hours: _____   min: _____

NOTES:

# Recipe: _____

## Ingredients _____

_____  _____
_____  _____
_____  _____
_____  _____
_____  _____

## Directions _____

_____
_____
_____
_____
_____
_____
_____
_____
_____
_____
_____
_____
_____
_____
_____
_____
_____
_____
_____
_____

SERVES

2   4   6   8   10+

DIFFICULTY:

1   2   3   4   5

COOK TIME:

hours: _____   min: _____

PREP TIME:

hours: _____   min: _____

NOTES:

# Recipe: _____

## Ingredients

_____  _____
_____  _____
_____  _____
_____  _____
_____  _____

## Directions

_____
_____
_____
_____
_____
_____
_____
_____
_____
_____
_____
_____
_____
_____
_____
_____
_____
_____
_____

**SERVES**

2   4   6   8   10+

**DIFFICULTY:**

1   2   3   4   5

**COOK TIME:**

hours: _____   min: _____

**PREP TIME:**

hours: _____   min: _____

**NOTES:**

# Recipe: _____

## Ingredients

_____  _____
_____  _____
_____  _____
_____  _____
_____  _____
_____  _____

## Directions

_____
_____
_____
_____
_____
_____
_____
_____
_____
_____
_____
_____
_____
_____
_____
_____
_____
_____
_____
_____
_____

SERVES
2   4   6   8   10+

DIFFICULTY:
1   2   3   4   5

COOK TIME:
hours: _____   min: _____

PREP TIME:
hours: _____   min: _____

NOTES:

# Recipe: _____

## Ingredients

_____  _____
_____  _____
_____  _____
_____  _____

## Directions

_____
_____
_____
_____
_____
_____
_____
_____
_____
_____
_____
_____
_____
_____
_____
_____
_____
_____
_____
_____
_____
_____

**SERVES**

2   4   6   8   10+

**DIFFICULTY:**

1   2   3   4   5

**COOK TIME:**

hours: _____   min: _____

**PREP TIME:**

hours: _____   min: _____

**NOTES:**

# Recipe: _____

## Ingredients

_____  _____
_____  _____
_____  _____
_____  _____
_____  _____

## Directions

_____
_____
_____
_____
_____
_____
_____
_____
_____
_____
_____
_____
_____
_____
_____
_____
_____
_____
_____
_____
_____

**SERVES**
2   4   6   8   10+

**DIFFICULTY:**
1   2   3   4   5

**COOK TIME:**
hours: _____   min: _____

**PREP TIME:**
hours: _____   min: _____

**NOTES:**

# Recipe: _____

## Ingredients

_____    _____
_____    _____
_____    _____
_____    _____

## Directions

_____
_____
_____
_____
_____
_____
_____
_____
_____
_____
_____
_____
_____
_____
_____
_____
_____
_____
_____
_____

**SERVES**

2   4   6   8   10+

**DIFFICULTY:**

1   2   3   4   5

**COOK TIME:**

hours: _____   min: _____

**PREP TIME:**

hours: _____   min: _____

**NOTES:**

# Recipe: _____

## Ingredients

_____  _____
_____  _____
_____  _____
_____  _____
_____  _____

## Directions

_____
_____
_____
_____
_____
_____
_____
_____
_____
_____
_____
_____
_____
_____
_____
_____
_____
_____
_____
_____
_____

**SERVES**
2   4   6   8   10+

**DIFFICULTY:**
1   2   3   4   5

**COOK TIME:**
hours: _____   min: _____

**PREP TIME:**
hours: _____   min: _____

**NOTES:**

# Recipe: _____

## Ingredients

_____  _____

_____  _____

_____  _____

_____  _____

## Directions

_____

_____

_____

_____

_____

_____

_____

_____

_____

_____

_____

_____

_____

_____

_____

_____

_____

_____

_____

**SERVES**

2   4   6   8   10+

**DIFFICULTY:**

1   2   3   4   5

**COOK TIME:**

hours: _____   min: _____

**PREP TIME:**

hours: _____   min: _____

**NOTES:**

# Recipe: _____

## ———— Ingredients ————

_____  _____
_____  _____
_____  _____
_____  _____
_____  _____
_____  _____

## Directions ————

_____
_____
_____
_____
_____
_____
_____
_____
_____
_____
_____
_____
_____
_____
_____
_____
_____
_____
_____

DIFFICULTY:
1   2   3   4   5

COOK TIME:
hours: _____   min: _____

PREP TIME:
hours: _____   min: _____

NOTES:

# Recipe: _____

## Ingredients

_____  _____
_____  _____
_____  _____
_____  _____
_____  _____

## Directions

_____
_____
_____
_____
_____
_____
_____
_____
_____
_____
_____
_____
_____
_____
_____
_____
_____
_____
_____
_____
_____

**SERVES**
2   4   6   8   10+

**DIFFICULTY:**
1   2   3   4   5

**COOK TIME:**
hours: _____   min: _____

**PREP TIME:**
hours: _____   min: _____

**NOTES:**

# Recipe: _____

## Ingredients

_____  _____
_____  _____
_____  _____
_____  _____

## Directions

_____
_____
_____
_____
_____
_____
_____
_____
_____
_____
_____
_____
_____
_____
_____
_____
_____
_____
_____
_____
_____
_____
_____
_____

SERVES
2  4  6  8  10+

DIFFICULTY:
1  2  3  4  5

COOK TIME:
hours: _____  min: _____

PREP TIME:
hours: _____  min: _____

NOTES:

# Recipe: _____

## Ingredients

_____    _____
_____    _____
_____    _____
_____    _____
_____    _____

## Directions

_____
_____
_____
_____
_____
_____
_____
_____
_____
_____
_____
_____
_____
_____
_____
_____
_____
_____
_____
_____
_____
_____

SERVES

2   4   6   8   10+

DIFFICULTY:

1   2   3   4   5

COOK TIME:

hours: _____   min: _____

PREP TIME:

hours: _____   min: _____

NOTES:

# Recipe: _____

## Ingredients

_____  _____
_____  _____
_____  _____
_____  _____
_____  _____

## Directions

_____
_____
_____
_____
_____
_____
_____
_____
_____
_____
_____
_____
_____
_____
_____
_____
_____
_____
_____
_____
_____

**SERVES**
2   4   6   8   10+

**DIFFICULTY:**
1   2   3   4   5

**COOK TIME:**
hours: _____   min: _____

**PREP TIME:**
hours: _____   min: _____

**NOTES:**

# Recipe: _____

## Ingredients

_____  _____
_____  _____
_____  _____
_____  _____
_____  _____

## Directions

_____
_____
_____
_____
_____
_____
_____
_____
_____
_____
_____
_____
_____
_____
_____
_____
_____
_____
_____
_____
_____

**SERVES**
2   4   6   8   10+

**DIFFICULTY:**
1   2   3   4   5

**COOK TIME:**
hours: _____   min: _____

**PREP TIME:**
hours: _____   min: _____

**NOTES:**

# Recipe: _____

## Ingredients

_____  _____
_____  _____
_____  _____
_____  _____
_____  _____
_____  _____

## Directions

_____
_____
_____
_____
_____
_____
_____
_____
_____
_____
_____
_____
_____
_____
_____
_____
_____
_____
_____

**SERVES**
2   4   6   8   10+

**DIFFICULTY:**
1   2   3   4   5

**COOK TIME:**
hours: ____   min: ____

**PREP TIME:**
hours: ____   min: ____

**NOTES:**

# Recipe: _____

## Ingredients

_____  _____
_____  _____
_____  _____
_____  _____

## Directions

_____
_____
_____
_____
_____
_____
_____
_____
_____
_____
_____
_____
_____
_____
_____
_____
_____
_____
_____
_____
_____

SERVES
2   4   6   8   10+

DIFFICULTY:
1   2   3   4   5

COOK TIME:
hours: _____  min: _____

PREP TIME:
hours: _____  min: _____

NOTES:

# Recipe: _____

## Ingredients

_____  _____
_____  _____
_____  _____
_____  _____
_____  _____

## Directions

_____
_____
_____
_____
_____
_____
_____
_____
_____
_____
_____
_____
_____
_____
_____
_____
_____
_____
_____
_____
_____
_____
_____

SERVES
2   4   6   8   10+

DIFFICULTY:
1   2   3   4   5

COOK TIME:
hours: _____   min: _____

PREP TIME:
hours: _____   min: _____

NOTES:

# Recipe: _____

## — Ingredients —

_____  _____
_____  _____
_____  _____
_____  _____
_____  _____

## Directions ——

_____
_____
_____
_____
_____
_____
_____
_____
_____
_____
_____
_____
_____
_____
_____
_____
_____
_____
_____
_____

SERVES

2   4   6   8   10+

DIFFICULTY:

1   2   3   4   5

COOK TIME:

hours: _____   min: _____

PREP TIME:

hours: _____   min: _____

NOTES:

# Recipe: _____

## Ingredients

_____  _____
_____  _____
_____  _____
_____  _____
_____  _____

## Directions

_____
_____
_____
_____
_____
_____
_____
_____
_____
_____
_____
_____
_____
_____
_____
_____
_____
_____
_____
_____
_____
_____

**SERVES**
2  4  6  8  10+

**DIFFICULTY:**
1  2  3  4  5

**COOK TIME:**
hours: ____  min: ____

**PREP TIME:**
hours: ____  min: ____

**NOTES:**

# Recipe: _____

## — Ingredients —

_____  _____
_____  _____
_____  _____
_____  _____

## Directions

_____
_____
_____
_____
_____
_____
_____
_____
_____
_____
_____
_____
_____
_____
_____
_____
_____
_____
_____

**SERVES**

2   4   6   8   10+

**DIFFICULTY:**

1   2   3   4   5

**COOK TIME:**

hours: _____   min: _____

**PREP TIME:**

hours: _____   min: _____

**NOTES:**

# Recipe: _____

## — Ingredients —

_____   _____
_____   _____
_____   _____
_____   _____
_____   _____
_____   _____

## Directions

_____
_____
_____
_____
_____
_____
_____
_____
_____
_____
_____
_____
_____
_____
_____
_____
_____
_____
_____
_____
_____

**SERVES**
2   4   6   8   10+

**DIFFICULTY:**
1   2   3   4   5

**COOK TIME:**
hours: _____   min: _____

**PREP TIME:**
hours: _____   min: _____

**NOTES:**

# Recipe: _____

## Ingredients

_____      _____
_____      _____
_____      _____
_____      _____
_____      _____

## Directions

_____
_____
_____
_____
_____
_____
_____
_____
_____
_____
_____
_____
_____
_____
_____
_____
_____
_____
_____
_____

**SERVES**

2   4   6   8   10+

**DIFFICULTY:**

1   2   3   4   5

**COOK TIME:**

hours: _____ min: _____

**PREP TIME:**

hours: _____ min: _____

**NOTES:**

# Recipe: _____

## Ingredients

_____  _____
_____  _____
_____  _____
_____  _____
_____  _____

## Directions

_____
_____
_____
_____
_____
_____
_____
_____
_____
_____
_____
_____
_____
_____
_____
_____
_____
_____
_____

SERVES
2   4   6   8   10+

DIFFICULTY:
1   2   3   4   5

COOK TIME:
hours: _____   min: _____

PREP TIME:
hours: _____   min: _____

NOTES:

# Recipe: _____

## — Ingredients —

_____  _____
_____  _____
_____  _____
_____  _____

## Directions _____

_____
_____
_____
_____
_____
_____
_____
_____
_____
_____
_____
_____
_____
_____
_____
_____
_____
_____
_____
_____

**SERVES**
2   4   6   8   10+

**DIFFICULTY:**
1   2   3   4   5

**COOK TIME:**
hours: _____   min: _____

**PREP TIME:**
hours: _____   min: _____

**NOTES:**

# Recipe: _____

## Ingredients

_____  _____
_____  _____
_____  _____
_____  _____
_____  _____
_____  _____

## Directions

_____
_____
_____
_____
_____
_____
_____
_____
_____
_____
_____
_____
_____
_____
_____
_____
_____
_____
_____
_____
_____
_____
_____

SERVES
2  4  6  8  10+

DIFFICULTY:
1  2  3  4  5

COOK TIME:
hours: _____  min: _____

PREP TIME:
hours: _____  min: _____

NOTES:

# Recipe: _____

## Ingredients

_____  _____
_____  _____
_____  _____
_____  _____

## Directions

_____
_____
_____
_____
_____
_____
_____
_____
_____
_____
_____
_____
_____
_____
_____
_____
_____
_____
_____

SERVES
2   4   6   8   10+

DIFFICULTY:
1   2   3   4   5

COOK TIME:
hours: _____   min: _____

PREP TIME:
hours: _____   min: _____

NOTES:

# Recipe: _____

## ─── Ingredients ───

_____  _____
_____  _____
_____  _____
_____  _____
_____  _____

## Directions ───

_____
_____
_____
_____
_____
_____
_____
_____
_____
_____
_____
_____
_____
_____
_____
_____
_____
_____
_____
_____
_____
_____

SERVES
2  4  6  8  10+

DIFFICULTY:
1  2  3  4  5

COOK TIME:
hours: _____  min: _____

PREP TIME:
hours: _____  min: _____

NOTES:

# Recipe: _____

## Ingredients

_____  _____
_____  _____
_____  _____
_____  _____

## Directions

_____
_____
_____
_____
_____
_____
_____
_____
_____
_____
_____
_____
_____
_____
_____
_____
_____
_____
_____
_____
_____

SERVES

2   4   6   8   10+

DIFFICULTY:

1   2   3   4   5

COOK TIME:

hours: _____   min: _____

PREP TIME:

hours: _____   min: _____

NOTES:

# Recipe: _____

## ──── Ingredients ────

_____  _____
_____  _____
_____  _____
_____  _____
_____  _____

## Directions

SERVES
2   4   6   8   10+

DIFFICULTY:
1   2   3   4   5

COOK TIME:
hours: _____   min: _____

PREP TIME:
hours: _____   min: _____

NOTES:

# Recipe: _____

## Ingredients

_____  _____
_____  _____
_____  _____
_____  _____
_____  _____

## Directions

_____
_____
_____
_____
_____
_____
_____
_____
_____
_____
_____
_____
_____
_____
_____
_____
_____
_____
_____
_____

**SERVES**

2   4   6   8   10+

**DIFFICULTY:**

1   2   3   4   5

**COOK TIME:**

hours: _____   min: _____

**PREP TIME:**

hours: _____   min: _____

**NOTES:**

# Recipe: _____

## — Ingredients —

_____    _____
_____    _____
_____    _____
_____    _____
_____    _____
_____    _____

## Directions

_____
_____
_____
_____
_____
_____
_____
_____
_____
_____
_____
_____
_____
_____
_____
_____
_____
_____
_____
_____
_____
_____

**SERVES**
2   4   6   8   10+

**DIFFICULTY:**
1   2   3   4   5

**COOK TIME:**
hours: _____   min: _____

**PREP TIME:**
hours: _____   min: _____

**NOTES:**

# Recipe: _____

## Ingredients

_____    _____
_____    _____
_____    _____
_____    _____

## Directions

_____
_____
_____
_____
_____
_____
_____
_____
_____
_____
_____
_____
_____
_____
_____
_____
_____
_____
_____

**SERVES**

2   4   6   8   10+

**DIFFICULTY:**

1   2   3   4   5

**COOK TIME:**

hours: _____   min: _____

**PREP TIME:**

hours: _____   min: _____

**NOTES:**

# Recipe: _____

## Ingredients

_____  _____
_____  _____
_____  _____
_____  _____
_____  _____

## Directions

_____
_____
_____
_____
_____
_____
_____
_____
_____
_____
_____
_____
_____
_____
_____
_____
_____
_____
_____
_____
_____
_____
_____
_____
_____
_____

SERVES
2   4   6   8   10+

DIFFICULTY:
1   2   3   4   5

COOK TIME:
hours: _____   min: _____

PREP TIME:
hours: _____   min: _____

NOTES:

# Recipe: _____

## — Ingredients —

_____   _____
_____   _____
_____   _____
_____   _____
_____   _____

## Directions

_____
_____
_____
_____
_____
_____
_____
_____
_____
_____
_____
_____
_____
_____
_____
_____
_____
_____
_____

**SERVES**

2   4   6   8   10+

**DIFFICULTY:**

1   2   3   4   5

**COOK TIME:**

hours: _____   min: _____

**PREP TIME:**

hours: _____   min: _____

**NOTES:**

# Recipe: _____

## Ingredients

_____  _____
_____  _____
_____  _____
_____  _____
_____  _____

## Directions

_____
_____
_____
_____
_____
_____
_____
_____
_____
_____
_____
_____
_____
_____
_____
_____
_____
_____
_____
_____
_____
_____

**SERVES**
2   4   6   8   10+

**DIFFICULTY:**
1   2   3   4   5

**COOK TIME:**
hours: _____   min: _____

**PREP TIME:**
hours: _____   min: _____

**NOTES:**

# Recipe: _____

## Ingredients

_____  _____
_____  _____
_____  _____
_____  _____

## Directions

_____
_____
_____
_____
_____
_____
_____
_____
_____
_____
_____
_____
_____
_____
_____
_____
_____
_____
_____
_____

SERVES

2   4   6   8   10+

DIFFICULTY:

1   2   3   4   5

COOK TIME:

hours: _____   min: _____

PREP TIME:

hours: _____   min: _____

NOTES:

# Recipe: _____

## Ingredients

_____  _____
_____  _____
_____  _____
_____  _____
_____  _____

## Directions

_____
_____
_____
_____
_____
_____
_____
_____
_____
_____
_____
_____
_____
_____
_____
_____
_____
_____
_____
_____
_____
_____
_____
_____

**SERVES**

2   4   6   8   10+

**DIFFICULTY:**

1   2   3   4   5

**COOK TIME:**

hours: _____   min: _____

**PREP TIME:**

hours: _____   min: _____

**NOTES:**

# Recipe: _____

## Ingredients

_____  _____
_____  _____
_____  _____
_____  _____
_____  _____

## Directions

_____
_____
_____
_____
_____
_____
_____
_____
_____
_____
_____
_____
_____
_____
_____
_____
_____
_____
_____
_____
_____
_____

**SERVES**

2  4  6  8  10+

**DIFFICULTY:**

1  2  3  4  5

**COOK TIME:**

hours: _____   min: _____

**PREP TIME:**

hours: _____   min: _____

**NOTES:**

# Recipe: _____

## Ingredients

_____  
_____  
_____  
_____  
_____  
_____  

## Directions

_____  
_____  
_____  
_____  
_____  
_____  
_____  
_____  
_____  
_____  
_____  
_____  
_____  
_____  
_____  
_____  
_____  
_____  
_____  
_____  
_____  
_____  

**SERVES**  
2   4   6   8   10+

**DIFFICULTY:**  
1   2   3   4   5

**COOK TIME:**  
hours: _____   min: _____

**PREP TIME:**  
hours: _____   min: _____

**NOTES:**

# Recipe: _____

## — Ingredients —

_____  _____
_____  _____
_____  _____
_____  _____
_____  _____

## Directions

_____
_____
_____
_____
_____
_____
_____
_____
_____
_____
_____
_____
_____
_____
_____
_____
_____
_____
_____
_____
_____

**SERVES**
2   4   6   8   10+

**DIFFICULTY:**
1   2   3   4   5

**COOK TIME:**
hours: _____   min: _____

**PREP TIME:**
hours: _____   min: _____

**NOTES:**

# Recipe: _____

## Ingredients

_____  _____
_____  _____
_____  _____
_____  _____
_____  _____
_____  _____

## Directions

_____
_____
_____
_____
_____
_____
_____
_____
_____
_____
_____
_____
_____
_____
_____
_____
_____
_____
_____
_____
_____
_____
_____

**SERVES**
2   4   6   8   10+

**DIFFICULTY:**
1   2   3   4   5

**COOK TIME:**
hours: _____   min: _____

**PREP TIME:**
hours: _____   min: _____

**NOTES:**

# Recipe: _____

## Ingredients

_____  _____
_____  _____
_____  _____
_____  _____
_____  _____

## Directions

_____
_____
_____
_____
_____
_____
_____
_____
_____
_____
_____
_____
_____
_____
_____
_____
_____
_____
_____
_____
_____

**SERVES**

2   4   6   8   10+

**DIFFICULTY:**

1   2   3   4   5

**COOK TIME:**

hours: _____   min: _____

**PREP TIME:**

hours: _____   min: _____

**NOTES:**

# Recipe: _____

## Ingredients

_____  _____
_____  _____
_____  _____
_____  _____
_____  _____

## Directions

_____
_____
_____
_____
_____
_____
_____
_____
_____
_____
_____
_____
_____
_____
_____
_____
_____
_____
_____
_____

SERVES

2   4   6   8   10+

DIFFICULTY:

1   2   3   4   5

COOK TIME:

hours: _____   min: _____

PREP TIME:

hours: _____   min: _____

NOTES:

# Recipe: _____

## Ingredients

_____  _____
_____  _____
_____  _____
_____  _____
_____  _____

## Directions

_____
_____
_____
_____
_____
_____
_____
_____
_____
_____
_____
_____
_____
_____
_____
_____
_____
_____
_____
_____
_____
_____

SERVES

2   4   6   8   10+

DIFFICULTY:

1   2   3   4   5

COOK TIME:

hours: _____   min: _____

PREP TIME:

hours: _____   min: _____

NOTES:

# Recipe: _____

## Ingredients

_____    _____
_____    _____
_____    _____
_____    _____
_____    _____

## Directions

_____
_____
_____
_____
_____
_____
_____
_____
_____
_____
_____
_____
_____
_____
_____
_____
_____
_____
_____
_____
_____
_____

SERVES
2   4   6   8   10+

DIFFICULTY:
1   2   3   4   5

COOK TIME:
hours: _____   min: _____

PREP TIME:
hours: _____   min: _____

NOTES:

# Recipe: _____

## — Ingredients —

_____  _____
_____  _____
_____  _____
_____  _____

## Directions

_____
_____
_____
_____
_____
_____
_____
_____
_____
_____
_____
_____
_____
_____
_____
_____
_____
_____
_____
_____
_____

SERVES

2   4   6   8   10+

DIFFICULTY:

1   2   3   4   5

COOK TIME:

hours: _____   min: _____

PREP TIME:

hours: _____   min: _____

NOTES:

# Recipe: _____

## Ingredients

_____  _____
_____  _____
_____  _____
_____  _____
_____  _____
_____  _____

## Directions

_____
_____
_____
_____
_____
_____
_____
_____
_____
_____
_____
_____
_____
_____
_____
_____
_____
_____
_____
_____

SERVES
2   4   6   8   10+

DIFFICULTY:
1   2   3   4   5

COOK TIME:
hours: _____   min: _____

PREP TIME:
hours: _____   min: _____

NOTES:

# Recipe: _____

## Ingredients

_____  _____

_____  _____

_____  _____

_____  _____

## Directions

_____

_____

_____

_____

_____

_____

_____

_____

_____

_____

_____

_____

_____

_____

_____

_____

_____

_____

_____

_____

_____

_____

_____

_____

_____

_____

_____

_____

**SERVES**

2   4   6   8   10+

**DIFFICULTY:**

1   2   3   4   5

**COOK TIME:**

hours: _____   min: _____

**PREP TIME:**

hours: _____   min: _____

**NOTES:**

# Recipe: _____

## Ingredients

_____  _____
_____  _____
_____  _____
_____  _____
_____  _____

## Directions

_____
_____
_____
_____
_____
_____
_____
_____
_____
_____
_____
_____
_____
_____
_____
_____
_____
_____
_____

SERVES
2   4   6   8   10+

DIFFICULTY:
1   2   3   4   5

COOK TIME:
hours: _____   min: _____

PREP TIME:
hours: _____   min: _____

NOTES:

# Recipe: _____

## ——— Ingredients ———

_____  _____
_____  _____
_____  _____
_____  _____

## Directions ———

_____
_____
_____
_____
_____
_____
_____
_____
_____
_____
_____
_____
_____
_____
_____
_____
_____
_____
_____

SERVES

2   4   6   8   10+

DIFFICULTY:

1   2   3   4   5

COOK TIME:

hours: _____   min: _____

PREP TIME:

hours: _____   min: _____

NOTES:

# Recipe: _____

## ——— Ingredients ———

_____  _____
_____  _____
_____  _____
_____  _____
_____  _____
_____  _____

## Directions ———

_____
_____
_____
_____
_____
_____
_____
_____
_____
_____
_____
_____
_____
_____
_____
_____
_____
_____
_____
_____
_____

SERVES
2   4   6   8   10+

DIFFICULTY:
1   2   3   4   5

COOK TIME:
hours: _____   min: _____

PREP TIME:
hours: _____   min: _____

NOTES:

# Recipe: _____

## — Ingredients —

_____  _____
_____  _____
_____  _____
_____  _____
_____  _____

## Directions

_____
_____
_____
_____
_____
_____
_____
_____
_____
_____
_____
_____
_____
_____
_____
_____
_____
_____
_____
_____
_____
_____
_____

**SERVES**

2   4   6   8   10+

**DIFFICULTY:**

1   2   3   4   5

**COOK TIME:**

hours: _____   min: _____

**PREP TIME:**

hours: _____   min: _____

**NOTES:**

# Recipe: _____

## Ingredients

_____  _____
_____  _____
_____  _____
_____  _____
_____  _____
_____  _____

## Directions

_____
_____
_____
_____
_____
_____
_____
_____
_____
_____
_____
_____
_____
_____
_____
_____
_____
_____
_____
_____
_____
_____
_____
_____
_____
_____

SERVES
2   4   6   8   10+

DIFFICULTY:
1   2   3   4   5

COOK TIME:
hours: _____   min: _____

PREP TIME:
hours: _____   min: _____

NOTES:

# Recipe: _____

## Ingredients

_____   _____
_____   _____
_____   _____
_____   _____
_____   _____

## Directions

_____
_____
_____
_____
_____
_____
_____
_____
_____
_____
_____
_____
_____
_____
_____
_____
_____
_____
_____
_____

**SERVES**
2   4   6   8   10+

**DIFFICULTY:**
1   2   3   4   5

**COOK TIME:**
hours: _____   min: _____

**PREP TIME:**
hours: _____   min: _____

**NOTES:**

# Recipe:

## Ingredients

_____
_____
_____
_____
_____

_____
_____
_____
_____

## Directions

_____
_____
_____
_____
_____
_____
_____
_____
_____
_____
_____
_____
_____
_____
_____
_____
_____
_____
_____
_____
_____
_____

SERVES
2   4   6   8   10+

DIFFICULTY:
1   2   3   4   5

COOK TIME:
hours: ____   min: ____

PREP TIME:
hours: ____   min: ____

NOTES:

# Recipe: _____

## Ingredients

_____  _____
_____  _____
_____  _____
_____  _____
_____  _____

## Directions

_____
_____
_____
_____
_____
_____
_____
_____
_____
_____
_____
_____
_____
_____
_____
_____
_____
_____
_____
_____

SERVES
2  4  6  8  10+

DIFFICULTY:
1  2  3  4  5

COOK TIME:
hours: _____  min: _____

PREP TIME:
hours: _____  min: _____

NOTES:

# Recipe: _____

## Ingredients

_____  _____
_____  _____
_____  _____
_____  _____
_____  _____
_____  _____

## Directions

SERVES
2   4   6   8   10+

DIFFICULTY:
1   2   3   4   5

COOK TIME:
hours: _____   min: _____

PREP TIME:
hours: _____   min: _____

NOTES:

# Recipe: _____

## Ingredients

_____    _____
_____    _____
_____    _____
_____    _____
_____    _____
_____    _____

## Directions

_____
_____
_____
_____
_____
_____
_____
_____
_____
_____
_____
_____
_____
_____
_____
_____
_____
_____
_____
_____

**SERVES**

2   4   6   8   10+

**DIFFICULTY:**

1   2   3   4   5

**COOK TIME:**

hours: _____   min: _____

**PREP TIME:**

hours: _____   min: _____

**NOTES:**

# Recipe: _____

## Ingredients

_____  _____
_____  _____
_____  _____
_____  _____
_____  _____

## Directions

_____
_____
_____
_____
_____
_____
_____
_____
_____
_____
_____
_____
_____
_____
_____
_____
_____
_____
_____
_____
_____

SERVES
2   4   6   8   10+

DIFFICULTY:
1   2   3   4   5

COOK TIME:
hours: ____   min: ____

PREP TIME:
hours: ____   min: ____

NOTES:

# Recipe: _____

## Ingredients

_____ _____
_____ _____
_____ _____
_____ _____

## Directions

_____
_____
_____
_____
_____
_____
_____
_____
_____
_____
_____
_____
_____
_____
_____
_____
_____
_____
_____
_____
_____

SERVES

2   4   6   8   10+

DIFFICULTY:

1   2   3   4   5

COOK TIME:

hours: _____   min: _____

PREP TIME:

hours: _____   min: _____

NOTES:

# Recipe: _____

## Ingredients

_____  _____
_____  _____
_____  _____
_____  _____
_____  _____
_____  _____

## Directions

_____
_____
_____
_____
_____
_____
_____
_____
_____
_____
_____
_____
_____
_____
_____
_____
_____
_____
_____
_____
_____
_____
_____
_____
_____
_____

**SERVES**
2   4   6   8   10+

**DIFFICULTY:**
1   2   3   4   5

**COOK TIME:**
hours: _____   min: _____

**PREP TIME:**
hours: _____   min: _____

**NOTES:**

# Recipe: _____

## Ingredients

_____  _____
_____  _____
_____  _____
_____  _____
_____  _____

## Directions

_____
_____
_____
_____
_____
_____
_____
_____
_____
_____
_____
_____
_____
_____
_____
_____
_____
_____
_____
_____
_____

**SERVES**

2    4    6    8    10+

**DIFFICULTY:**

1    2    3    4    5

**COOK TIME:**

hours: _____    min: _____

**PREP TIME:**

hours: _____    min: _____

**NOTES:**

# Recipe: _____

## Ingredients

_____  _____
_____  _____
_____  _____
_____  _____
_____  _____

## Directions

_____
_____
_____
_____
_____
_____
_____
_____
_____
_____
_____
_____
_____
_____
_____
_____
_____
_____
_____
_____
_____
_____

**SERVES**
2   4   6   8   10+

**DIFFICULTY:**
1   2   3   4   5

**COOK TIME:**
hours: ____   min: ____

**PREP TIME:**
hours: ____   min: ____

**NOTES:**

# Recipe: _____

## Ingredients

_____    _____
_____    _____
_____    _____
_____    _____
_____    _____

## Directions

_____
_____
_____
_____
_____
_____
_____
_____
_____
_____
_____
_____
_____
_____
_____
_____
_____
_____
_____
_____
_____

**SERVES**

2   4   6   8   10+

**DIFFICULTY:**

1   2   3   4   5

**COOK TIME:**

hours: _____   min: _____

**PREP TIME:**

hours: _____   min: _____

**NOTES:**

# Recipe: _____

## Ingredients

_____  _____
_____  _____
_____  _____
_____  _____
_____  _____
_____  _____

## Directions

_____
_____
_____
_____
_____
_____
_____
_____
_____
_____
_____
_____
_____
_____
_____
_____
_____
_____
_____
_____
_____
_____
_____
_____
_____

SERVES
2   4   6   8   10+

DIFFICULTY:
1   2   3   4   5

COOK TIME:
hours: _____   min: _____

PREP TIME:
hours: _____   min: _____

NOTES:

# Recipe: _____

## Ingredients

_____  _____
_____  _____
_____  _____
_____  _____
_____  _____

## Directions

_____
_____
_____
_____
_____
_____
_____
_____
_____
_____
_____
_____
_____
_____
_____
_____
_____
_____
_____
_____
_____

SERVES

2   4   6   8   10+

DIFFICULTY:

1   2   3   4   5

COOK TIME:

hours: _____   min: _____

PREP TIME:

hours: _____   min: _____

NOTES:

# Recipe: _____

## ─── Ingredients ───

_____    _____
_____    _____
_____    _____
_____    _____
_____    _____

## Directions

_____
_____
_____
_____
_____
_____
_____
_____
_____
_____
_____
_____
_____
_____
_____
_____
_____
_____
_____
_____
_____
_____

SERVES
2   4   6   8   10+

DIFFICULTY:
1   2   3   4   5

COOK TIME:
hours: _____   min: _____

PREP TIME:
hours: _____   min: _____

NOTES:

# Recipe: _____

## — Ingredients —

_____   _____
_____   _____
_____   _____
_____   _____
_____   _____

## Directions ——

_____
_____
_____
_____
_____
_____
_____
_____
_____
_____
_____
_____
_____
_____
_____
_____
_____
_____
_____
_____

**SERVES**
2   4   6   8   10+

**DIFFICULTY:**
1   2   3   4   5

**COOK TIME:**
hours: _____   min: _____

**PREP TIME:**
hours: _____   min: _____

**NOTES:**

# Recipe: _____

## ───── Ingredients ─────

_____  _____
_____  _____
_____  _____
_____  _____
_____  _____
_____  _____

## Directions ─────

_____
_____
_____
_____
_____
_____
_____
_____
_____
_____
_____
_____
_____
_____
_____
_____
_____
_____
_____
_____
_____
_____

**SERVES**
2   4   6   8   10+

**DIFFICULTY:**
1   2   3   4   5

**COOK TIME:**
hours: _____   min: _____

**PREP TIME:**
hours: _____   min: _____

**NOTES:**

# Recipe: _____

## — Ingredients —

_____  _____
_____  _____
_____  _____
_____  _____
_____  _____

## Directions

_____
_____
_____
_____
_____
_____
_____
_____
_____
_____
_____
_____
_____
_____
_____
_____
_____
_____

SERVES
2   4   6   8   10+

DIFFICULTY:
1   2   3   4   5

COOK TIME:
hours: _____   min: _____

PREP TIME:
hours: _____   min: _____

NOTES:

# Recipe: _____

## Ingredients

_____  _____
_____  _____
_____  _____
_____  _____

## Directions

_____
_____
_____
_____
_____
_____
_____
_____
_____
_____
_____
_____
_____
_____
_____
_____
_____
_____
_____
_____
_____
_____

SERVES
2   4   6   8   10+

DIFFICULTY:
1   2   3   4   5

COOK TIME:
hours: _____   min: _____

PREP TIME:
hours: _____   min: _____

NOTES:

# Recipe: _____

## Ingredients

_____  _____
_____  _____
_____  _____
_____  _____
_____  _____

## Directions

_____
_____
_____
_____
_____
_____
_____
_____
_____
_____
_____
_____
_____
_____
_____
_____
_____
_____
_____
_____
_____

SERVES

2   4   6   8   10+

DIFFICULTY:

1   2   3   4   5

COOK TIME:

hours: _____   min: _____

PREP TIME:

hours: _____   min: _____

NOTES:

# Recipe: _____

## Ingredients

_____  _____
_____  _____
_____  _____
_____  _____
_____  _____

## Directions

_____
_____
_____
_____
_____
_____
_____
_____
_____
_____
_____
_____
_____
_____
_____
_____
_____
_____
_____
_____
_____
_____
_____
_____
_____
_____

SERVES
2  4  6  8  10+

DIFFICULTY:
1   2   3   4   5

COOK TIME:
hours: _____   min: _____

PREP TIME:
hours: _____   min: _____

NOTES:

# Recipe: _____

## Ingredients

_____  _____
_____  _____
_____  _____
_____  _____
_____  _____

## Directions

_____
_____
_____
_____
_____
_____
_____
_____
_____
_____
_____
_____
_____
_____
_____
_____
_____
_____
_____
_____

SERVES
2   4   6   8   10+

DIFFICULTY:
1   2   3   4   5

COOK TIME:
hours: _____   min: _____

PREP TIME:
hours: _____   min: _____

NOTES:

# Recipe: _____

## Ingredients

_____

_____

_____

_____

_____

_____

_____

_____

## Directions

SERVES

2  4  6  8  10+

DIFFICULTY:

1  2  3  4  5

COOK TIME:

hours: _____  min: _____

PREP TIME:

hours: _____  min: _____

NOTES:

# Recipe: _____

## Ingredients

_____ _____
_____ _____
_____ _____
_____ _____
_____ _____

## Directions

_____
_____
_____
_____
_____
_____
_____
_____
_____
_____
_____
_____
_____
_____
_____
_____
_____
_____
_____
_____
_____
_____

**SERVES**
2   4   6   8   10+

**DIFFICULTY:**
1   2   3   4   5

**COOK TIME:**
hours: _____   min: _____

**PREP TIME:**
hours: _____   min: _____

**NOTES:**

# Recipe: _____

## ─── Ingredients ───

_____    _____

_____    _____

_____    _____

_____    _____

_____    _____

## Directions ───

_____

_____

_____

_____

_____

_____

_____

_____

_____

_____

_____

_____

_____

_____

_____

_____

_____

_____

_____

_____

_____

_____

_____

**SERVES**

2   4   6   8   10+

**DIFFICULTY:**

1   2   3   4   5

**COOK TIME:**

hours: _____    min: _____

**PREP TIME:**

hours: _____    min: _____

**NOTES:**

# Recipe: _____

## Ingredients

_____  _____
_____  _____
_____  _____
_____  _____
_____  _____

## Directions

_____
_____
_____
_____
_____
_____
_____
_____
_____
_____
_____
_____
_____
_____
_____
_____
_____
_____
_____
_____
_____

SERVES

2   4   6   8   10+

DIFFICULTY:

1   2   3   4   5

COOK TIME:

hours: _____  min: _____

PREP TIME:

hours: _____  min: _____

NOTES:

# Recipe: _____

## Ingredients

_____  _____
_____  _____
_____  _____
_____  _____
_____  _____

## Directions

_____
_____
_____
_____
_____
_____
_____
_____
_____
_____
_____
_____
_____
_____
_____
_____
_____
_____
_____
_____

**SERVES**
2   4   6   8   10+

**DIFFICULTY:**
1   2   3   4   5

**COOK TIME:**
hours: _____   min: _____

**PREP TIME:**
hours: _____   min: _____

**NOTES:**

# Recipe: _____

## — Ingredients —

_____    _____
_____    _____
_____    _____
_____    _____

## Directions

_____
_____
_____
_____
_____
_____
_____
_____
_____
_____
_____
_____
_____
_____
_____
_____
_____
_____
_____
_____
_____
_____

**SERVES**

2  4  6  8  10+

**DIFFICULTY:**

1  2  3  4  5

**COOK TIME:**

hours: _____   min: _____

**PREP TIME:**

hours: _____   min: _____

**NOTES:**

Made in the USA
Monee, IL
08 August 2022

11205155R00063